Disney

Sofia the First

Illustrated by Patricia Phillipson and the Disney Storybook Art Team

 publications international, ltd.

Sofia has a lot to learn about being a princess! Find Sofia and these other things in the throne room:

Sofia's amulet

King Roland's crown

royal desserts

Cedric's wand

Sofia's throne

Amber's fan

With her magical amulet, Sofia can talk to animals! Will you find these fresh fruits she shares with her new friends?

strawberries

pineapple

bananas

orange

apple

grapes

At Royal Prep, Sofia learns that part of being a princess is doing your very best in every subject. Can you find these school supplies?

paintbrush

this book

globe

this scroll

teacher's wand

Amber's bag

Sofia knows that part of being a good princess is being a good sport. While everyone has fun, look for these things that a royal recess requires:

soccer ball

basketball

flying horseshoe

croquet ball

volleyball

discus

In the palace or on the paths of Peppertree Forest, Sofia loves an adventure! Look for these things at the Buttercups' campsite:

map

backpack

first-aid kit

these logs

manual

canteen

Sofia's tea party is a smashing success. Can you find these butterflies in Sofia's secret garden?

Sofia's old friends are just as important as her new friends. Find these things at her royal sleepover:

slippers

hairbrush

this pillow

cello

these pajamas

overnight bag

As Sofia learns the ABCs of being a princess, she needs all the help she can get! Lend a hand by finding these helpful friends and family members:

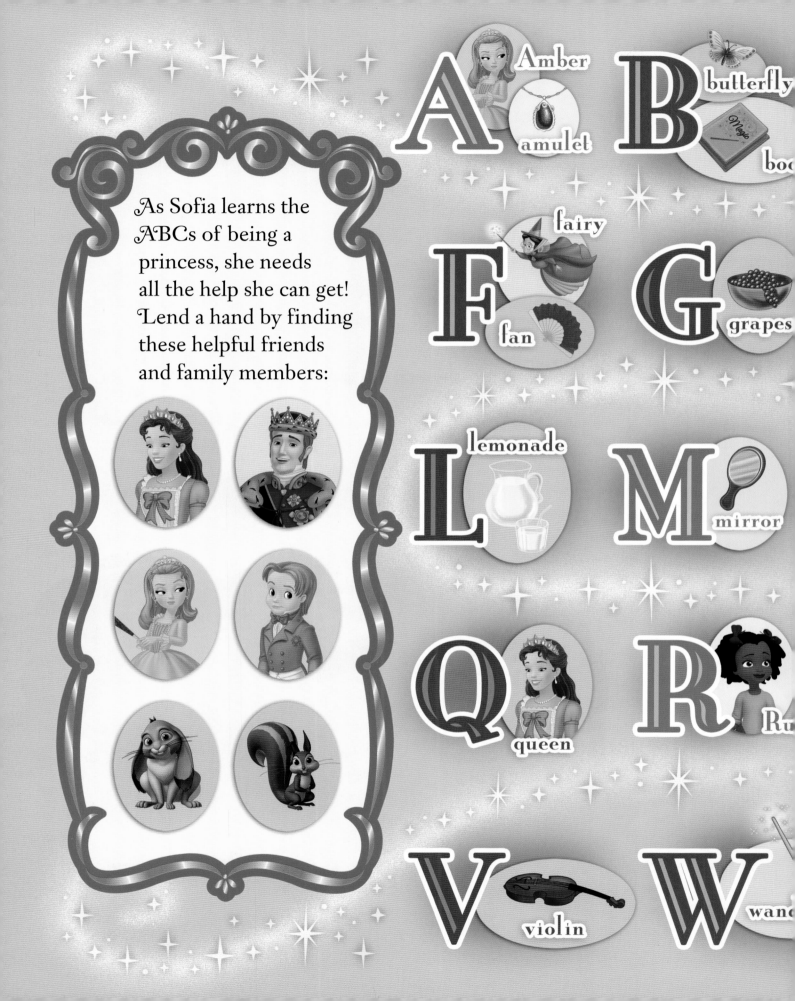

A Amber
amulet

B butterfly
Magic book

F fairy
fan

G grapes

L lemonade

M mirror

Q queen

R Ru

V violin

W wand

C  Clover

D dress

E earrings eyes

H horseshoe
heart

I invitation

J James
jump rope

K king

N nest

O orange

P pillow
popcorn

S Sofia

T tea
tiara

U umbrella
unicorn

Whatnaught

X xylophone

Y yo-yo

Z Zandar

Queen rhymes with green. Return to Sofia's family to find these royal rhymes:

- gown/crown
- crow/bow
- chair/hair
- fairies/berries
- suit/boot
- tea/key

Go back to Sofia's picnic with her new friends and look for these healthy goodies:

- green pepper
- carrots
- lettuce
- red cabbage
- broccoli
- corn

Royal Prep is a fun place for a princess to learn. Look for these shapes in Sofia's classroom:

- circle
- heart
- rectangle
- star
- oval
- triangle

Race back to the royal recess and spot these recess activities:

- bouncing
- reaching
- catching
- jumping
- throwing
- kicking

Pairs are things that come in twos. Hike back to the Buttercups to find these pairs:

- pair of acorns
- pair of birdhouses
- pair of hot dogs
- pair of birds
- pair of squirrels
- pair of bouquets

Flutter back to Sofia's tea party to count these things:

- 1 teapot
- 2 spoons
- 3 Good Fairies
- 4 princesses
- 5 tea cakes
- 6 teacups

Sofia's sleepover is the perfect party. Can you find these things that start with the letter **p**?

- pinecones
- popcorn
- pajamas
- princess
- pitcher
- pet

Flip back to the alphabet and find the letters that spell

SOFIA